First published in 1996 by Leopard Books,
a division of Random House UK Ltd,
20 Vauxhall Bridge Road, London SW1V 2SA

Text © 1996 Judy Allen
Illustrations © 1996 Alan Baker

ISBN 0 7529 0172 9

Printed in Singapore

HEDGEHOG

in the Garden

JUDY ALLEN AND ALAN BAKER

LEOPARD

There were fourteen guests at Grandma's birthday party and each one had brought her a present.

Mick was impressed.

Mick's mother was surprised. "We've all given you plants," she said.

Grandma was pleased. "No one can ever have too many plants," she beamed.

"Mick," said Grandma. "Will you go out to the garden shed for me?"

"All right," said Mick. "What for?"

"You'll find some big china pot-holders in there. Will you fetch them? Here's a torch – it's dark outside."

When Mick got outside he found it wasn't just dark –
it was quiet and creepy as well.

Inside the shed it was even creepier.

Mick heard a weird sound. It was a rustling, grumbling,
sniffing sound. Something was in the shed with him.

Mick didn't like it. He clattered out of the shed
and shut the door behind him.
Then he heard the rustling, grumbling, sniffing sound again.
The thing was not shut inside the shed.
It was outside, with him.

Mick pointed the torch at the dark flowerbeds.
One of the plants was moving, just a little,
as though something was pushing past it.
Mick didn't wait to find out what it was.
He fled towards the light of the kitchen door.

Mick explained to Grandma that there was a goblin in her garden – or perhaps a gremlin – or a very small alien.

"None of those," said Grandma. "Just a friend of mine," and she began to put some dog food on to a saucer.

Mick followed Grandma into the garden and watched as she set the saucer down, just where the kitchen light shone on the grass.

"Look!" said Grandma.

A bush rustled – and then a hedgehog came grumbling and sniffing out from under it.

"She lives under the shed," said Grandma. "She hibernates there all winter, and sleeps there by day in summer."

"She's noisy," said Mick.

"She sniffs and snorts to smell out her food," explained Grandma. "She eats the things that spoil my plants – caterpillars and beetles and slugs."

"Why do you give her dog food as well?" asked Mick.
"Because she visits all the gardens around,"
said Grandma, "but if she knows she'll get an
extra snack here, she'll always come back."

The hedgehog began to eat, and Grandma nudged
Mick. "Look what's following her," she whispered.
     Rustling out from under the bush
came four baby hedgehogs.
     "They're about five weeks old,"
said Grandma. "For the first four
weeks they stayed in the nest
and fed on their mother's
milk. Now they're bigger,
and ready for
solid food."

Then Grandma pointed to the little pond.
"See those big stones?" she said. "I've put them there
so that if the hedgehogs fall in the water – which
they sometimes do – they can climb out again."

Suddenly there was a scrabbling noise – and then a
thud and the cat from next door leapt onto the fence.
Before Mick or Grandma could move, it jumped down
and ran towards the hedgehog family.

Immediately, all five hedgehogs tucked in
their heads and rolled themselves up. The cat
stood and stared. Instead of five small animals,
all it could see was five bristly balls.

Grandma clapped her hands at the cat and shooed it away, back over the fence and into its own garden.

"The mother would have been safe," said Grandma, as all the hedgehogs began to unroll again. "But the young ones have softer spines and weaker muscles, and the cat might have been able to kill them. They have a nice life, really, but there are dangers."

"Ponds and cats," said Mick, as the mother hedgehog led her babies onto the nearest flowerbed.

"And dogs, and foxes," said Grandma. "And poison."

"Poison?" said Mick.

"Some people put out poison to kill slugs or beetles," said Grandma.

"And the hedgehogs eat the poisoned slugs?"

"It can happen," said Grandma. "There – our friends have gone hunting – we must go back to the party."

As Mick and Grandma went back into the kitchen,
they met Mick's mother.

"Where are the pots?" she asked.

"Oh," said Mick. "Sorry, I forgot the pots."

"Never mind," she said, "I'll get them."

Mick followed his mother. She stood in the middle of the dark garden and listened.

"There's something out here," she said, "making a funny rustling, grumbling, sniffing noise."

"I know," said Mick. "It's hedgehogs. If you like, I'll tell you all about them. I know *a lot* about hedgehogs."